Soccer Science

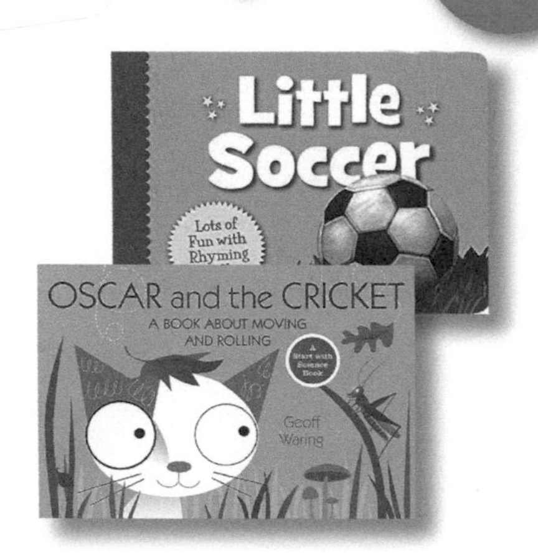

Description

Students explore the phenomenon of how soccer players get a soccer ball to go where they want it to go. They read a nonfiction book about motion and observe and describe patterns of forces and motion (e.g., the harder you kick, the faster the ball goes). Then, they apply their understandings about forces and motion to design a game that uses pushes and pulls.

Alignment With the *Next Generation Science Standards*

Performance Expectation

K-PS2-1: Plan and conduct an investigation to compare the effects of different strengths or different directions of pushes and pulls on the motion of an object.

Science and Engineering Practices	Disciplinary Core Ideas	Crosscutting Concepts
Planning and Carrying Out Investigations With guidance, plan and conduct an investigation in collaboration with peers. Obtaining, Evaluating, and Communicating Information Read grade-appropriate texts and/or use media to obtain scientific and/or technical information to determine patterns in and/or evidence about the natural and designed world(s). Communicate information or design ideas and/or solutions with others in oral and/or written forms using models, drawings, writing, or numbers that provide detail about scientific ideas, practices, and/or design ideas.	PS2.A: Forces and Motion Pushes and pulls can have different strengths and directions. Pushing or pulling on an object can change the speed or direction of its motion and can start or stop it. PS2.B: Types of Interactions When objects touch or collide, they push on one another and can change motion. PS3.C: Relationship Between Energy and Forces A bigger push or pull makes things speed up or slow down more quickly.	Cause and Effect Events have causes that generate observable patterns. Scale, Proportion, and Quantity Relative scales allow objects and events to be compared and described (e.g., bigger and smaller, hotter and colder, faster and slower). Patterns Patterns in the natural and human-designed world can be observed, used to describe phenomena, and used as evidence.

Note: The activities in this lesson will help students move toward the performance expectation listed, which is the goal after multiple activities. However, the activities will not by themselves be sufficient to reach the performance expectation.

Featured Picture Books

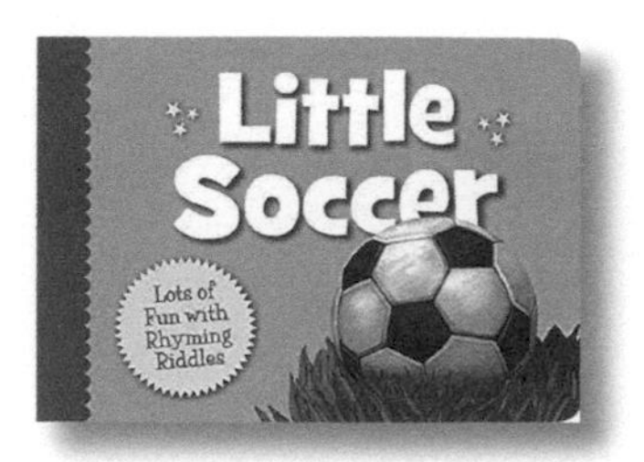

TITLE: ***Little Soccer***
AUTHOR: **Brad Herzog**
ILLUSTRATOR: **Doug Bowles**
PUBLISHER: **Sleeping Bear Press**
YEAR: **2011**
GENRE: **Non-Narrative Information**
SUMMARY: *Fun rhyming riddles ask the reader to identify different things related to soccer, such as "It rolls and bounces, flies through the air. Players chase it from here to there." On the following page, the answer is provided, "Soccer Ball."*

TITLE: ***Oscar and the Cricket: A Book About Moving and Rolling***
AUTHOR: **Geoff Waring**
ILLUSTRATOR: **Geoff Waring**
PUBLISHER: **Candlewick Press**
YEAR: **2009**
GENRE: **Narrative Information**
SUMMARY: *Oscar is a curious kitten. When he finds a round red ball, he is full of questions about moving and rolling. Luckily, Cricket knows the answers! With the help of his friend, Oscar learns how objects start moving, stop moving, speed up, slow down, and change direction.*

Time Needed

This lesson will take several class periods. Suggested scheduling is as follows:

Session 1: Engage with Little Soccer Read-Aloud and FIFA Videos

Session 2: Explore with Little Soccer Demonstration and Little Soccer Challenges

Session 3: Explain with Our Observations and Oscar and the Cricket Read-Aloud

Session 4: Elaborate with Design a Game and Evaluate with Design a Game Student Page

Materials

For Little Soccer Challenges (per pair)

- 1 mini soccer ball (or other small foam ball)
- 2 mini traffic cones or orange plastic cups
- Masking tape
- Tape measure
- Soccer Goal Sheet

For Oscar and the Cricket Stop-and-Try-It Read Aloud

- 1 mini soccer ball
- 2 mini traffic cones or orange plastic cups

Ordering Information

Mini sports balls (soccer)
www.amazon.com/gp/product/B01BGHMXJG/ref=ppx_yo_dt_b_search_asin_title?ie=UTF8&psc=1

Mini orange traffic cones
www.orientaltrading.com/orange-traffic-cones-a2-20_298.fltr?keyword=traffic+cones

For Design a Game (per pair)

- 1 mini soccer ball
- 2 plastic cups large enough for the ball to fit in
- 2 pipe cleaners
- 2 craft sticks

Student Pages

- Soccer Goal Sheet
- Little Soccer Challenges
- Design a Game
- STEM Everywhere

SAFETY

- Wear safety glasses with side shields or safety goggles during the setup, hands-on, and takedown segments of the activity.
- Use caution when using sharp or pointed materials (e.g., pipe cleaners, craft sticks) because they can cut or puncture skin.
- Use caution when working with a soccer ball because it can be a trip-and-fall hazard if it is on the floor.
- Make sure the trajectory for projectiles (soccer ball) are marked off and do not allow anyone to stand in their path. Also remove any fragile materials in the trajectory path.
- Wash your hands with soap and water immediately after completing this activity.

Background for Teachers

According to the Fédération Internationale de Football Association (FIFA), there are nearly 300 million athletes around the world playing organized football with an estimated 3.5 billion fans, making it the most popular sport on the planet! And while most of the world refers to this sport as football, in the United States it is commonly called soccer. Many children are familiar with the sport of soccer, whether they play on an organized team or just kick a soccer ball at recess or at home. This lesson provides students with opportunities to recognize simple cause-and-effect relationships between force and motion in the context of this popular sport. The Framework suggests that in early grades students experience the phenomenon that pushes and pulls can be used to change the motion of an object—to make it go faster or slower, change direction, start moving, or stop moving. After reading a book of riddles about soccer and sharing their own experiences with soccer, students watch some videos of professional soccer players controlling the ball, scoring goals, and blocking goals. The question is then posed—how do these soccer players make the ball go where they want it to go? To figure this out, students participate in an investigation where they attempt different challenges with a mini soccer ball and a goal (made with two small cones or cups). These explorations give them the opportunity to observe the effects of different strengths and directions of pushes and pulls.

Students learn that they can use forces (pushes and pulls) to make the ball start moving, slow down, speed up, change direction, or stop moving. They read a nonfiction book that explains the basic cause-and-effect relationships between forces and motion. Then, students apply what they have learned to design their own game using the mini soccer ball and other classroom supplies. To evaluate their learning, they explain in words and pictures how to play their game and how pushes and pulls are used in the game.

Learning Progressions

Below are the DCI grade band endpoints for grades K–2 and 3–5. These are provided to show how student understanding of the DCIs in this lesson will progress in future grade levels.

DCIs	Grades K–2	Grades 3–5
PS2.A: Forces and Motion	• Pushes and pulls can have different strengths and directions. • Pushing or pulling on an object can change the speed or direction of its motion and can start or stop it.	• Each force acts on one particular object and has both strength and a direction. An object at rest typically has multiple forces acting on it, but they add to give zero net force on the object. Forces that do not sum to zero can cause changes in the object's speed or direction of motion. • The patterns of an object's motion in various situations can be observed and measured; when that past motion exhibits a regular pattern, future motion can be predicted from it.
PS2.B: Types of Interactions	• When objects touch or collide, they push on one another and can change motion.	• Objects in contact exert forces on each other.
PS3.C: Relationship Between Energy and Forces	• A bigger push or pull makes things go faster.	• When objects collide, the contact forces transfer energy so as to change the objects' motions.

Source: Willard, T., ed. 2015. The NSTA quick-reference guide to the NGSS: Elementary school. Arlington, VA: NSTA Press.

engage

Little Soccer Read-Aloud and FIFA Videos

Making Connections

Show students the cover of Little Soccer. Ask

? Have you ever played soccer? (Answers will vary.)

? Did you play on a team or on the playground or in your yard? (Answers will vary.)

? What is the object of the game (in other words, how do you win)? (Get the most points.)

? How do you get points? (Get the soccer ball in the goal.)

? What are some of the rules of soccer? (You can't touch the ball with your hands unless you are the goalie, if the ball goes off the field it is out of bounds, and so on.)

? What do soccer players wear? (shorts, tall socks, shin guards, cleats)

Connecting to the Common Core
Reading: Literature
Key Ideas and Details: K.1

Inferring

Explain that Little Soccer is a book of riddles. Tell students that after you read each riddle, they can guess the answer before you show them the answer on the following page. Read the book aloud, pausing to have students share their guesses for each riddle.

After reading, ask

- ? What are you wondering about soccer?
- ? Have you ever watched a professional soccer game? (Answers will vary.)
- ? What was it like? (Answers will vary.)
- ? How did the players start or stop the ball? (by kicking it, by dribbling it with their feet, by throwing it, by catching it)

Tell students that you have some videos of professional soccer players playing soccer, and while they watch you want them to think about the following question:

- ? How do soccer players get the ball to go where they want it to go?

Show some of the videos in the "Websites" section of this lesson, such as highlights from the 2019 Women's World Cup and "Impossible Saves."

After watching some of the videos, ask the question again:

- ? How do these players get the ball to go where they want it to go? (kick it, bounce it off their heads, the goal keepers stop it with their hands and throw it the direction they want it to go)

explore

Little Soccer Demonstration

Ahead of time, make copies of the Soccer Goal Sheet. Each pair of students will need one sheet.

Reread the last line of Little Soccer, "Now find a friend and a soccer ball. This great game is a thrill for all." Then, ask

Setting up the goal

- ? Who would like to play a game of "little soccer" with a friend?

Show students a foam mini soccer ball. Tell them that this is the ball they will use to do some soccer challenges with a partner. These challenges will give them an opportunity to observe the motion of the ball in a miniature soccer game. Show them two mini traffic cones and tell them that these will mark the goal. Model how the mini cones should be placed in the circles on the Soccer Goal sheet. Tell students that some youth soccer goals are 6 feet wide. You may want to use a tape measure or your floor tiles to measure this out to show students the size of an actual goal. Tell students that since they are using a mini soccer ball instead of a real soccer ball, their goal will also be on a smaller scale, approximately 4 ½ inches wide.

Little Soccer Challenges

> **CCC: Scale, Proportion, and Quantity**
> Relative scales allow objects and events to be compared and described (e.g., bigger and smaller, hotter and colder, faster and slower).

Connecting to the Common Core
Mathematics
Measurement and Data: K.MD.1

Tell students that for these challenges, they will need a start line. The start line should be 24 inches from the goal. Model using a measuring tape to measure 24 inches from the goal and place an approximately 4-inch piece of masking tape parallel to the goal line.

Explain that they will be using their hands to make the ball move. Students can "kick" the ball with their fingers, but they are not allowed to throw the ball. One way to make sure they do not throw the ball is to tell students that they cannot use their thumbs when they "kick" the ball. Call on a student to be your partner. Have them sit behind the goal so they can stop the ball. Model how to "kick" the ball with your fingers by flicking it or pushing it with your fingers.

Little Soccer Challenges

Have students pair up and give them the Soccer Goal Sheet, two mini cones, a tape measure, and 4 inches of masking tape. Tell students that once they have their goal set up properly and the tape 24 inches from the goal, they will receive their soccer ball. To make this measuring process easier, you may want to place a mark on the tape measures at 24 inches or provide a string that is 24 inches long.

> **SEP: Planning and Carrying Out Investigations**
> With guidance, plan and conduct an investigation in collaboration with peers.

Give each student the Little Soccer Challenges student page, a clipboard, and a pencil. Announce each challenge one by one, making sure both students have had a chance to try it and mark down their results before moving on to the next one. Tell students that they are allowed to try multiple times. Before students begin Challenge 5, model how they can use their clipboards as a surface for the ball to bounce off by having a student hold a clipboard upright and rolling a ball into it.

Challenges from the student page:

1. Can you make the ball roll from the start line across the goal line?

2. Can you make the ball roll slower across the goal line?
3. Can you make the ball roll faster across the goal line?
4. Can you make the ball roll from the start line and stop before it goes across the goal line?
5. Can you make the ball bounce off of something and go across the goal line?

explain

Our Observations

After trying all of the challenges and putting the supplies away, bring students back together and ask

? How did you make the ball roll faster? ("kicked" it harder)

? How did you make the ball roll slower? ("kicked" it softer)

? Was it easier to make a goal when the ball was rolling faster or slower? (Answers will vary.)

? How did you get the ball to stop before it went across the goal line? (rolled it slowly, put my hand out to stop it)

? Were you able to get the ball to bounce off of something and go across the goal line? (Answers will vary.)

? What was the hardest challenge? (Answers will vary.)

? Did the ball hit anything it wasn't supposed to hit? If so, what happened? (Answers will vary.)

? Did the ball ever go where you didn't want it to go? (Students will likely say "yes.")

? How do you think soccer players get the ball to go where they want it to go? (they kick it hard or soft, they kick it in a certain direction)

CCC: Patterns
Patterns in the natural and human-designed world can be observed, used to describe phenomena, and used as evidence.

Oscar and the Cricket Read-Aloud

Determining Importance

Show students the cover of Oscar and the Cricket: A Book About Moving and Rolling. Tell students that as you read, you would like them to think about their experience with the Little Soccer Challenges. Read the entire book aloud, stopping occasionally to allow for student questions and discussion. Then, ask

? How was the book like your Little Soccer Challenges? (the ball stayed on the ground, it rolled, it stopped, it bounced and changed direction, it moved fast with a hard push and slow with a light push)

SEP: Obtaining, Evaluating, and Communicating Information
Read grade-appropriate texts to obtain scientific information to describe patterns in the natural world.

Connecting to the Common Core
Reading: Informational Text
Key Ideas and Details: K.3

Stop and Try It

Tell students that you are going to read the book again, but this time you are going to stop and try

some of the things illustrated in the book with the mini soccer ball and cones. Invite students to sit in a circle on the floor so they can all see the ball and cones. Stop after reading the following pages and have student volunteers demonstrate the situations that follow:

> **CCC: Cause and Effect**
> Events have causes that generate observable patterns.

Page 7: "Try pushing it with your paw." Have a student come up and demonstrate how they "kicked" the soccer ball. Explain that this "kick" is called a push. A push causes the ball to move away from you.

Page 9: "Why did it stop?" Have a student roll the ball lightly and watch it stop on its own. Ask

? Why does the ball eventually stop rolling? (Answers will vary.)

Explain that the ball eventually stops rolling because it rubs against the carpet. The carpet slows it down, just like the grass did in the book.

Page 11: "Try giving it a pull." Point out that in the illustration Oscar is pulling the branch. Explain that pulling is moving something toward you. Call on a student to demonstrate how they could pull the ball. Pulling it toward themselves on the floor or picking it up are both examples of pulling.

Page 15: "Bounce!" Invite a student to come up and demonstrate the ball bouncing off of something (the clipboard or one of the cones). Ask

? What happens when the ball hits something? (It bounces off and changes direction.)

Skip pages 16–21.

Page 22: "You gave it such a strong push." Call on a student to come up and demonstrate a strong push. (The ball has to stay on the ground.) Then, have the student give it a light push. Ask

? How does the strength of the push affect the motion of the ball? (The harder you push, the faster and farther it goes.)

Page 25: "But just then, a kitten put out a paw and the ball stopped." Invite two students up to demonstrate pushing and stopping the ball. One student can give it a push and the other can stop it with their hand. Ask

? Did the hand stop the ball slowly or quickly? (quickly)

Page 29: Remind students that at the beginning of the lesson, you asked the question, "How do soccer players get the ball to go where they want it to go?" As you read each section on pages 29 and 30 ("Getting going," "Keeping going," and "Stopping"), use the following explanations to guide your conversation.

"Getting going"—The players get the ball moving by kicking it (push) or the goalie can pick it up (pull) and then throw it out (push). The harder the kick (push), the faster and farther the ball goes. Players can kick hard or soft depending on how fast and far they want the ball to go.

> **CCC: Scale, Proportion, and Quantity**
> Relative scales allow objects and events to be compared and described (e.g., bigger and smaller, hotter and colder, faster and slower).

"Keeping going"—When the soccer ball is kicked (pushed), it moves in a straight line until it hits something (another player's foot, chest, or head; a goalie's hands; the goal post).

"Stopping"—A player can stop the ball by placing their foot on top of the ball, or a goalie can stop the ball by catching it.

After reading, ask

? What are some things you have learned about pushes and pulls? (Answers will vary.)

elaborate

Design a Game

Ask students if they have ever wondered how the game of soccer was invented. Tell them that soccer began over 2,000 years ago in ancient China. The game involved kicking an animal-hide ball into a net that was 30 feet off the ground. But England gets credit for setting up the first official rules for soccer, including not allowing the tripping of opponents or touching the ball with your hands. In the United States, we call it soccer, but in most of the world it is called football.

Explain that basketball was invented by a physical education teacher at a YMCA over 100 years ago. He wanted to come up with a game to occupy a group of rowdy kids. He needed it to be an indoor game because it was wintertime. He came up with the idea of nailing fruit baskets to a high railing in the gym. Players tried to throw a soccer ball into the basket. If they made a basket, they had to stop the game so that the janitor could climb up a ladder to retrieve the ball! After a while, they figured out that it would be easier to cut out the bottoms of the fruit baskets. Ask

? How do you think the game of basketball got its name? (They were throwing the ball into fruit baskets.)

Tell students that they now have the opportunity to use what they have learned about pushes and pulls to work in teams of two to design a brand-new game of their own using the mini soccer ball. Share the following guidelines:

1. Your game must have a way to score points.
2. Your game must use pushes and pulls.
3. You cannot touch the ball with your hands.
4. The ball cannot leave the ground.

Show students the supplies they can choose from to design their game (mini soccer ball, 2 plastic cups, 2 pipe cleaners, and 2 craft sticks). Ask the following questions and call on students to demonstrate:

Materials for Design a Game activity

? How could you use these materials to push the ball? (hit it with a craft stick, bump it with a cup, hit it with the pipe cleaner)

? How could you use these materials to pull the ball? (pull it toward you with a craft stick, put the upside-down cup over the ball and pull the cup toward you, loop the pipe cleaner and pull the ball in the loop toward you)

Tell students to think about how they would score points in the game and how someone would win the game. As they are working, they should think of a name for their game. The name should have to do with how the game is played or the equipment that is used.

Visit teams as they are working on their game. Ask

? How do you play your game?

? How do you score?

? How do you win?

? How do you push the ball in your game?

? How do you pull the ball in your game?

? How could you make your game easier, harder, or more fun?

evaluate

Design a Game Student Page

Connecting to the Common Core
Writing: Text Types and Purposes
Key Ideas and Details: K.2

Writing

When teams are finished designing their game, pass out the Design a Game student page to each student and discuss the following with the class:

? What would be a catchy name for your game? (Answers will vary.)

? How do you play the game? (Answers will vary.)

? How could you show how to play the game using a drawing? (Answers will vary.)

? What labels could you add to your drawing to help describe how the game is played? (ball, player, stick, etc.)

? How could arrows help someone understand how to play the game? (Arrows could be used to show the direction the ball moves.)

? What are some examples of pushes in your game? (Answers will vary.)

? What are some example of pulls in your game? (Answers will vary.)

SEP: Obtaining, Evaluating, and Communicating Information
Communicate information with others in oral and/or written forms using models, drawings, writing, or numbers that provide detail about scientific ideas.

Point out that there are multiple solutions to the challenge of designing a game using the materials provided. Then have students fill out the following information on the Design a Game student page:

1. Name of game
2. How do you play the game? Use drawings and labels.
3. Give an example of a push in your game.
4. Give an example of a pull in your game.

Finally, have teams teach others how to play their game!

STEM Everywhere

Give students the STEM Everywhere student page as a way to involve their families and extend their learning. They can do the activity with an adult helper and share their results with the class.

Opportunities for Differentiated Instruction

This box lists questions and challenges related to the lesson that students may select to research, investigate, or innovate. Students may also use the questions as examples to help them generate their own questions. These questions can help you move your students from the teacher-directed investigation to engaging in the science and engineering practices in a more student-directed format.

Extra Support

For students who are struggling to meet the lesson objectives, provide a question and guide them in the process of collecting research or helping them design procedures or solutions.

Extensions

For students with high interest or who have already met the lesson objectives, have them choose a question (or pose their own question), conduct their own research, and design their own procedures or solutions.

After selecting one of the questions in the box or formulating their own questions, students can individually or collaboratively make predictions, design investigations or surveys to test their predictions, collect evidence, devise explanations, design solutions, or examine related resources. They can communicate their findings through a science notebook, at a poster session or gallery walk, or by producing a media project.

Research

Have students brainstorm researchable questions:

- ? How are soccer balls made?
- ? How and when was baseball invented?
- ? Why is a football shaped the way it is?

Investigate

Have students brainstorm testable questions to be solved through science or math:

- ? What are all the different ways you can move a ball?
- ? How many times can you and a friend toss a ball to each other before it hits the ground?
- ? Circumference is the distance around a sphere. Can you place a variety of balls in order from the smallest circumference to the largest circumference?

Innovate

Have students brainstorm problems to be solved through engineering:

- ? Can you design a game using toy cars and ramps?
- ? Can you design a bowling game using everyday objects?
- ? Can you design an organizer to store sports equipment?

Websites

FIFA's YouTube Channel
www.youtube.com/user/FIFATV

Highlights from the Women's 2019 World Cup
www.fifa.com/womensworldcup/

"Impossible Saves" Video
www.youtube.com/watch?v=Ny2S4YURXBA

More Books to Read

Lindeen, M. 2018. *Speed*. Chicago: Norwood House Press.
Summary: This Beginning-to-Read book provides simple text and photographs that illustrate cause-and-effect relationships between forces and motion.

Stille, D. R. 2004. *Motion: Push and pull, fast and slow.* North Mankato, MN: Picture Window Books.
Summary: Simple text and vivid illustrations offer an introduction to basic force and motion concepts, such as inertia, gravity, and friction.

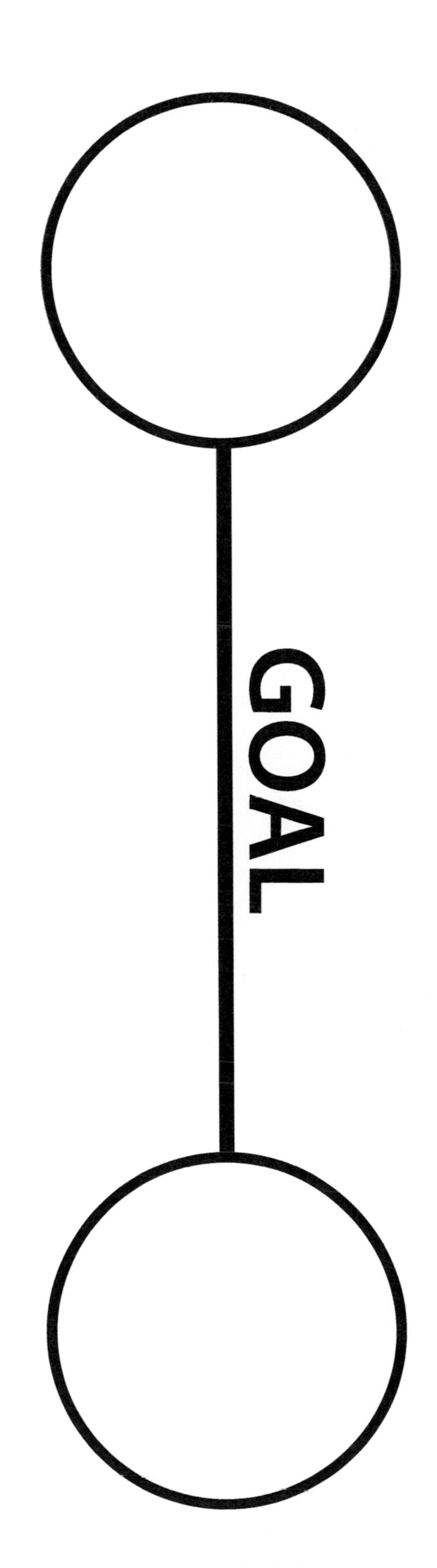
GOAL

Name: ____________________

Little Soccer Challenges

Can you do the challenges below using your finger to "kick" the ball?

1. Can you make the ball **roll** from the start line across the goal line?

☐ yes or ☐ no

2. Can you make the ball roll **slower** across the goal line?

☐ yes or ☐ no

3. Can you make the ball roll **faster** across the goal line?

☐ yes or ☐ no

4. Can you make the ball roll from the start line and **stop** before it goes across the goal line?

☐ yes or ☐ no

5. Can you make the ball **bounce** off of something and go across the goal line?

☐ yes or ☐ no

Name: ____________________

Design a Game

1. Name of game: ____________________

2. How do you play the game? Use drawings and labels.

3. Give an example of a **push** in your game.

____

____

4. Give an example of a **pull** in your game.

____

____

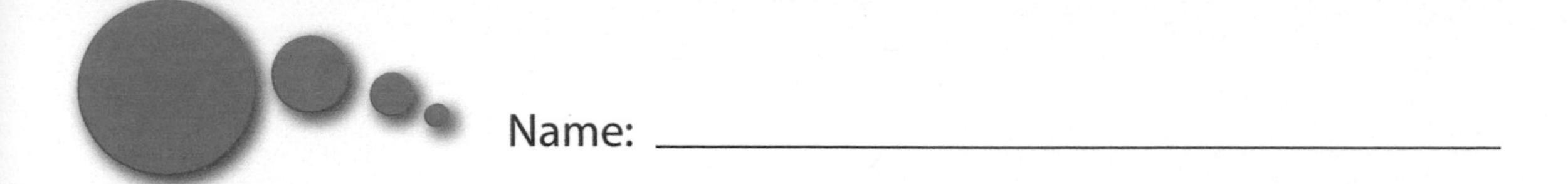

Name: ______________________________

STEM Everywhere

Dear Families,

At school, we have been learning about **how forces are used to play soccer.** Soccer players use *pushes* and *pulls* to make the ball start moving, stop moving, go fast, go slow, and change direction. To find out more, ask your learner the following questions and discuss their answers:

- What did you learn?
- What was your favorite part of the lesson?
- What are you still wondering?

At home, design a ball game together that uses pushes or pulls to score points. You can use any type of ball, and any common household items to safely move the ball. Have your learner use words and/or pictures to describe how the game is played in the box below.

Name of Game ______________________________